It's Easy To Play Pub Songs.

PUB SONGS

Wise Publications
London/New York/Sydney

Exclusive distributors:
Music Sales Limited
8/9 Frith Street, London W1V 5TZ, England.
Music Sales Pty Limited
120 Rothschild Avenue, Rosebery, NSW 2018, Australia.

This book © Copyright 1990 by
Wise Publications
UK ISBN 0.7119.1362.5.
Order No. AM69279
Compiled by Peter Evans
Arranged by Frank Booth
Music processed by Music Print
Typeset by Capital Setters

Music Sales' complete catalogue lists thousands of
titles and is free from your local music shop,
or direct from Music Sales Limited.
Please send £1.50 Cheque or Postal Order for postage to
Music Sales Limited, 8/9 Frith Street, London W1V 5TZ.

Printed in the United Kingdom by
Caligraving Limited, Thetford, Norfolk

Goodnight Sweetheart

Words & Music by Ray Noble,
Jimmy Campbell & Reg Connelly

Hold Me

Words & Music by Little Jack Little,
Dave Oppenheim & Ira Schuster

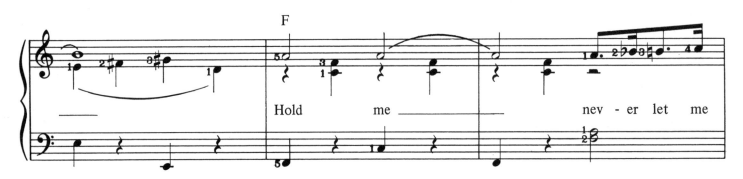

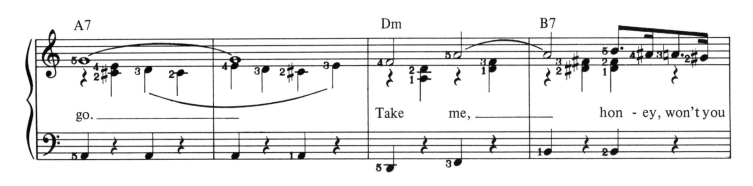

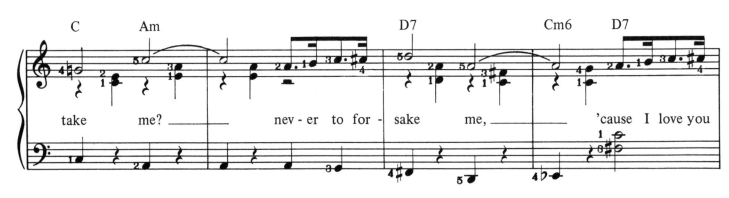

I Ain't Got Nobody
(And There's Nobody Cares For Me)

Words & Music by Roger Graham & Spencer Williams

Steady 2 beat

I Can't Give You Anything But Love

Words by Dorothy Fields
Music by Jimmy McHugh

al - ways pined for. Gee, I'd like to see you look - ing swell,

ba - by, Dia - mond brace - lets Wool - worth's does - n't sell,

ba - by. Till that luck - y day you know darned well,

ba - by, I can't give you an - y - thing but

love.

love.

If I Had My Way

Words by Lou Klein
Music by James Kendis

Jolly Good Company

Words & Music by Raymond Wallace

Lambeth Walk

Music by Noel Gay
Words by Douglas Furber & Arthur Rose

Lam - beth gal ____ with her lit - tle

Lam - beth pal, ____ you'll find ____ 'em all

do - in' the Lam - beth Walk.

Ev - 'ry - thing free ____ and ea - sy,

Do as you darn ____ well pleas - ey,

Leaning On A Lamp Post

Words & Music by Noel Gay

an - y - way I know that she'll try. Oh me, oh

my, I hope the lit - tle la - dy comes by. There's

no oth - er girl I could wait for, but

this one I'd break an - y date for, I

won't have to ask what she's late for; She'd

On A Slow Boat To China

Words & Music by Frank Loesser

weep-ing on the far-a-way shore. ____ Out on the bri-ny ____ with a

moon big and shi-ny, ____ melt-ing your heart of

stone; ____ I'd love to get you ____ on a

slow boat to Chi-na, ____ all to my-self a -

1. lone. **2.** - lone.

One! Two! Drink Up!

Words by Harry Lester, Charles Waugh & Ed Brown
Music by Wiga-Gabriel

Show Me The Way To Go Home

Words & Music by Irving King

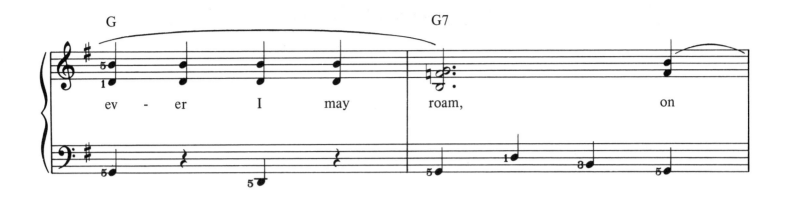

ev - er I may roam, on

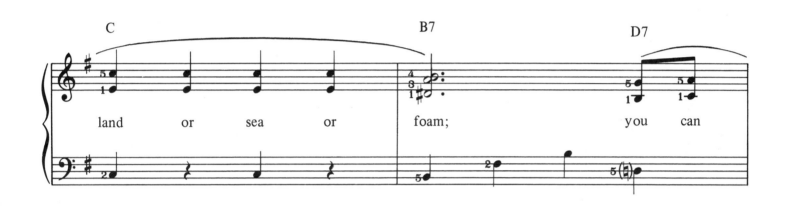

land or sea or foam; you can

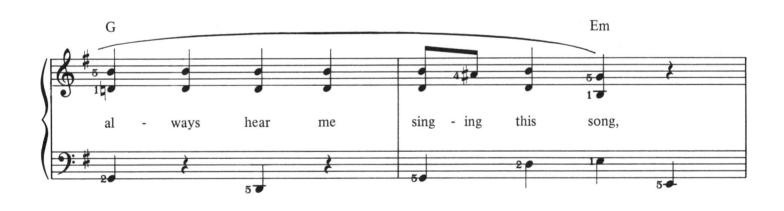

al - ways hear me sing - ing this song,

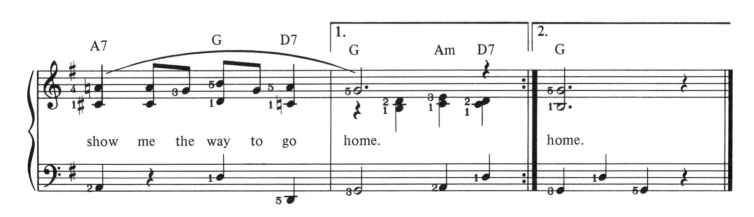

show me the way to go home. home.

Tennessee Waltz

Words & Music by Redd Stewart & Pee Wee King

I was waltz - ing with my dar - lin' to the

Ten - nes - see waltz when an old friend I hap - pened to

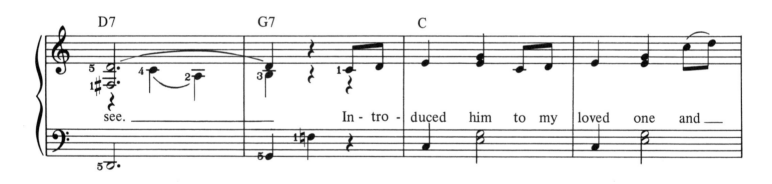

see. In - tro - duced him to my loved one and

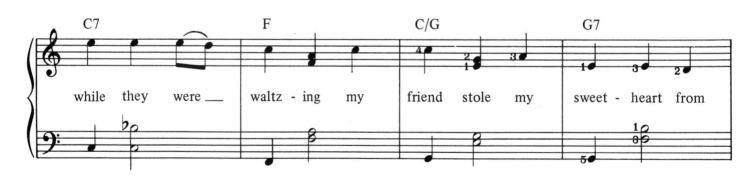

while they were waltz - ing my friend stole my sweet - heart from

me. ____ I re - mem - ber the night and the

Ten - nes - see waltz, now I know just how much I have

lost. ____ Yes I lost my lit - tle dar - lin' the ___

night they were ___ play - ing the beau - ti - ful Ten - nes - see

1.
waltz. I was

2.
waltz. ____

The Hokey Cokey

Words & Music by Jimmy Kennedy

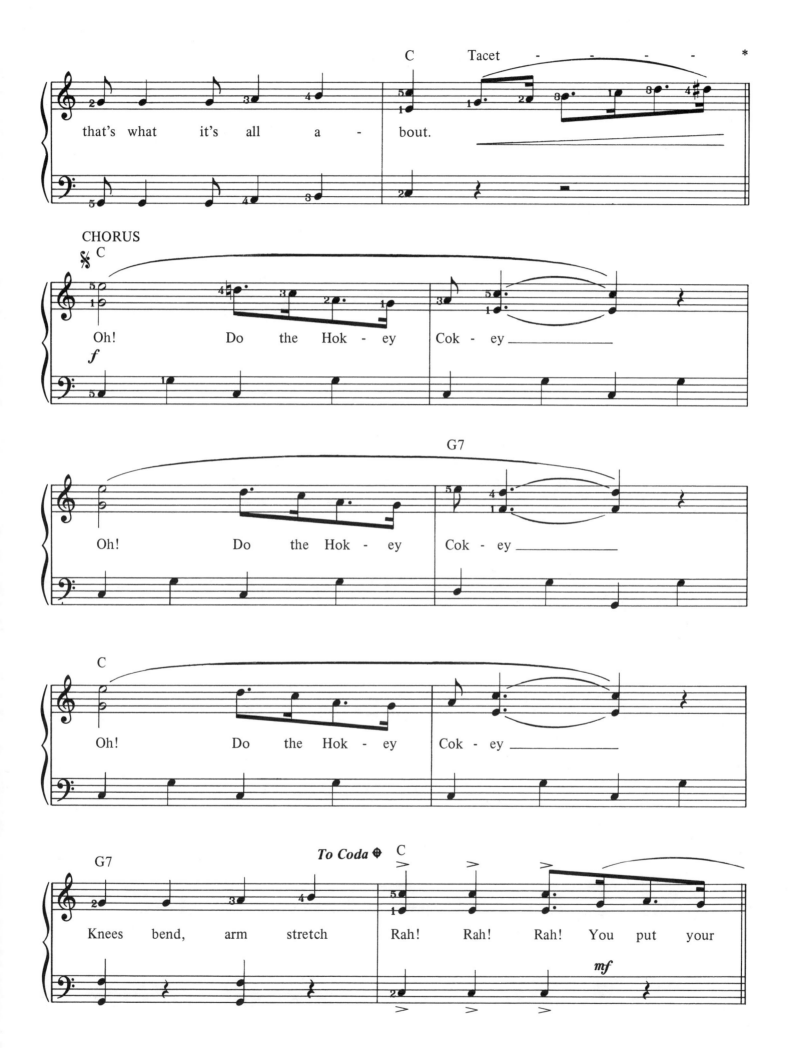

whole self in, whole self out,

in, out, in then you shake it all a - bout you

do the Hok - ey Cok - ey and you turn a - round ___

that's what it's all a - bout.

Rah! Rah! Rah!

The More We Are Together

Words & Music by Irving King

There Goes My Everything

Words & Music by Dallas Frazier

Together

Words & Music by B. G. Sylva,
Lew Brown & Ray Henderson

We'll Meet Again

Words & Music by Ross Parker & Hughie Charles

Moderately, with expression

We'll meet a - gain, don't know where, don't know when; but I know we'll meet a - gain some sun - ny day.

Keep smil - in' through just like you al - ways do, till the blue skies drive the dark clouds far a - way.

You Always Hurt
The One You Love

Words & Music by Doris Fisher & Allan Roberts

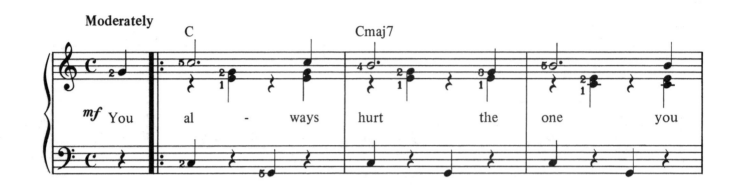

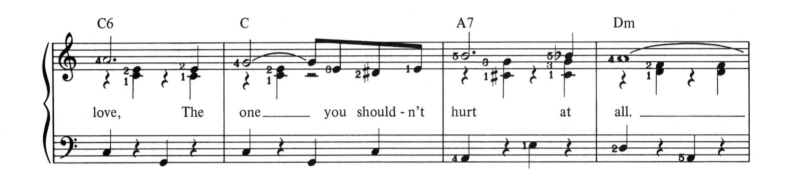

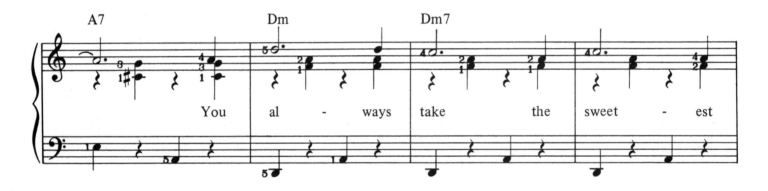

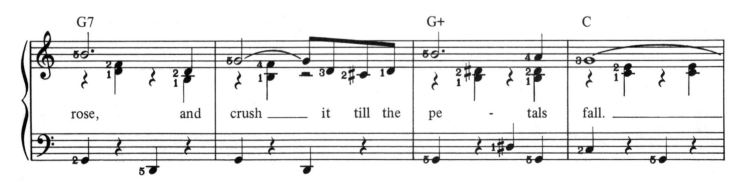

You al - ways break the kind - est
heart, with a hast - y word you can't re - call.
So if I broke your heart last
night, it's be - cause I love you most of
all. You
all.

You Are My Sunshine

Words & Music by Jimmie Davis & Charles Mitchell

CHORUS

43

You're Nobody Till Somebody Loves You

Words & Music by Russ Morgan,
Larry Stock & James Cavanaugh

Underneath The Arches

Words & Music by Bud Flanagan